BEAR'S
Special
BIRTHDAY

WRITTEN BY A.J. WOOD   ILLUSTRATIONS BY LORNA HUSSEY

mustard

Bear had a very special job.
He owned a bakery, and every morning
he would get up early and begin baking.

Bear could bake everything to perfection.
He baked bread and buns, pies and pastries,
and all sorts of shapes and sizes of biscuit.

He could make giant doughnuts with jam in the middle
and chocolate eclairs with extra chocolate.

But the things he made
best of all were...

CAKES!

Everyone loved Bear's cakes.

They would travel for miles to visit his bakery, and queue for ages to buy one of his fantastic cake creations. No-one in the world could bake cakes as delicious and splendid as Bear could.

Bear made his cakes in all shapes and sizes, in every colour and flavour you could imagine.

He could make cakes shaped like fish or birds...

He could make striped cakes, spotted cakes, BIG cakes and little cakes.

There was just the right cake
for everyone!

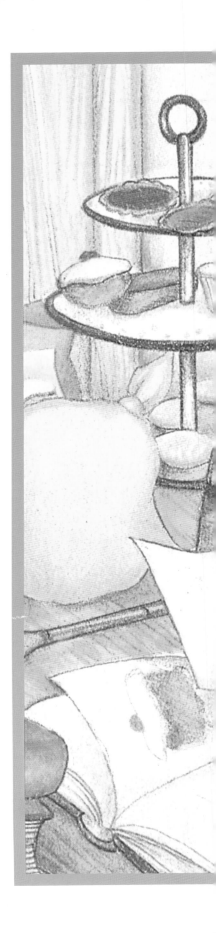

But there was just one problem —
Bear longed for someone to make HIM
a special surprise cake.
He looked at the calendar.
Soon it would be his birthday.
"It's no fun baking a cake for yourself!"
said Bear sadly.

Little did Bear know that his friends had
planned a surprise.
"We will make this a really special birthday,"
said Elephant.

CAKES

Recipes

First, they went to the bookshop
and bought a cookery book. Then they
went to the grocer's and bought all
the ingredients they needed.

Back in Elephant's kitchen they mixed everything together.

Everyone had their own ideas about how they
should decorate Bear's birthday cake.
"It must be the best surprise ever!"
they agreed...

...And it was!

This is a Mustard Book

Mustard is an imprint of Parragon

Parragon,

Queen Street House,

4 Queen Street, Bath BA1 1HE

Produced by the Templar Company plc,

Pippbrook Mill, London Road, Dorking, Surrey RH4 1JE

Text and design copyright © 1999 by the Templar Company plc

Illustrations copyright © 1994 by Lorna Hussey

All rights reserved.

ISBN 1-84164-046-8

Designed by Hayley Bebb

Edited by Dugald Steer

Printed in Singapore